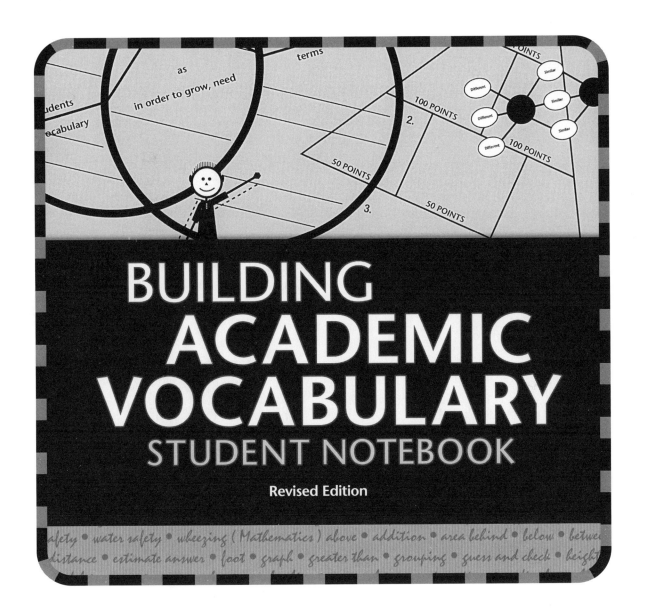

BUILDING
ACADEMIC
VOCABULARY
STUDENT NOTEBOOK

Revised Edition

This notebook belongs to:

ASCD | Alexandria, Virginia USA

1703 N. Beauregard St. • Alexandria, VA 22311-1714 USA
Telephone: 1-800 933 2723 or 1-703 578 9600 • Fax: 1-703 575 5400
Web site: www.ascd.org • E mail: member@ascd.org

Copyright © 2005, 2008 by the Association for Supervision and Curriculum Development,
1703 North Beauregard Street, Alexandria, VA 22311 1714 USA. All rights reserved.

Printed in the United States of America by Sheridan Books, Inc.
Chelsea, Michigan USA
October 2010
321120

ASCD Stock No: 109030

ISBN: 978-1-4166-0769-4

17   16   15   14   13   12   11   2 3 4 5 6 7 8 9 10 11 12

Dear Student,

These pages will help you keep a record of what you know about terms that are important in different subject areas. The terms have been chosen because they are used often in the subject area under which they are listed. Understanding these terms will help you become a more successful learner in that subject. You will notice that the pages in this notebook provide spaces for you to show what you know in several ways.

Below you will find a sample of a notebook page with the various spaces and areas noted and described for you.

First, you have a place to write the term, neatly and spelled correctly.

Next, describe what the term means. Don't just copy a definition from the dictionary. Instead, try to describe the term as you would to a friend.

This next space is where you draw what you understand about the term. Drawing pictures is a good way to show what you know, even if you aren't very good at drawing. In fact, simple pictures sometimes work better than words at conveying meaning.

The blank space is here so you can add anything else that will help you understand the term. You might, for example, draw another picture, use the word in a sentence, write an antonym or synonym, or list other words that come to mind when you think about this term.

This space allows you to add another word that will help you organize your academic vocabulary within a subject. For example, under the subject of math, you could use this space to write "geometry" or "fractions" to identify terms that belong to those subsets.

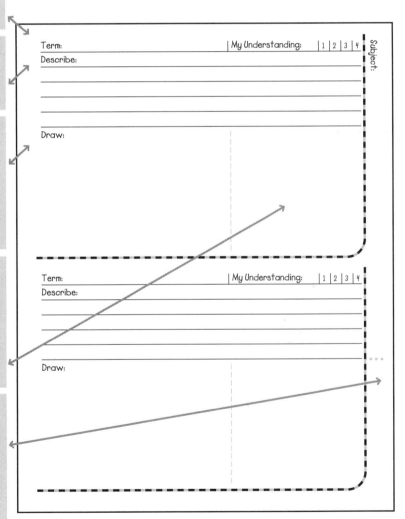

These numbers are here to help when you ask yourself how well you understand the term. Your teacher will let you know when to do this. Use the following guide to help you rate your level of understanding:

4	I understand even more about the term than I was taught.
3	I understand the term and I'm not confused about any part of what it means.
2	I'm a little unsure or confused about what the term means, but I have a general idea.
1	I'm very unsure or confused about the term. I really don't understand what it means yet.

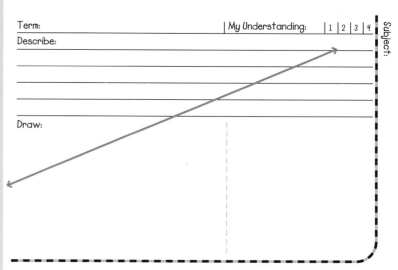

Term: _____ | My Understanding: | 1 | 2 | 3 | 4 | Subject:

Describe: _____

Draw:

You can use these pages to help you learn important terms. Read the tips below to get started. At the bottom of the page, you can add your own ideas for using these pages to increase your learning.

- Do everything you can to make sure the information that you have for a term is **correct** and that **it makes sense to you.** When you are confused or unsure about a term's meaning, ask for help.

- Dictionaries are great tools, but you don't talk or think like a dictionary—so don't copy definitions. Use definitions to help you **describe** the term. You want your description to be correct, but you also want it to sound the way you talk and think.

- When you first learn a term, write and draw what you understand at that time, but **then go back and add** more information or more pictures as you begin to understand the term even better.

- Don't worry about how well you draw, just try to show the basic meaning of the term. **Drawing helps you learn** because it makes you think in a different way. It is definitely worth the effort.

- **Show your ideas** to others and **get ideas** from them.

 Have fun with these pages!

Robert J. Marzano   Debra Pickering

Authors, *Building Academic Vocabulary Teacher's Manual*

Term: _____ | My Understanding: | 1 | 2 | 3 | 4 |

Subject:

Describe: _____

_____

_____

_____

_____

Draw:

Term: _____ | My Understanding: | 1 | 2 | 3 | 4 |

Describe: _____

_____

_____

_____

_____

Draw:

Subject:

| Term: | My Understanding: | 1 | 2 | 3 | 4 |

Describe:

_____

_____

_____

_____

_____

Draw:

| Term: | My Understanding: | 1 | 2 | 3 | 4 |

Describe:

_____

_____

_____

_____

_____

Draw:

Term: _____ | My Understanding: | 1 | 2 | 3 | 4 |

Describe: _____

_____

_____

_____

_____

Draw:

Term: _____ | My Understanding: | 1 | 2 | 3 | 4 |

Describe: _____

_____

_____

_____

_____

Draw:

Subject:

Term: _____ | My Understanding: | 1 | 2 | 3 | 4 |

Describe: _____
_____
_____
_____
_____

Draw:

Term: _____ | My Understanding: | 1 | 2 | 3 | 4 |

Describe: _____
_____
_____
_____
_____

Draw:

Term: _____ | My Understanding: | 1 | 2 | 3 | 4

Describe: _____

_____

_____

_____

Draw:

Subject:

Term: _____ | My Understanding: | 1 | 2 | 3 | 4

Describe: _____

_____

_____

_____

Draw:

Subject:

Term: _____ | My Understanding: | 1 | 2 | 3 | 4

Describe: _____

_____

_____

_____

_____

Draw:

Term: _____ | My Understanding: | 1 | 2 | 3 | 4

Describe: _____

_____

_____

_____

_____

Draw:

Term: _____ | My Understanding: | 1 | 2 | 3 | 4

Describe: _____

_____

_____

_____

_____

Draw:

Subject:

Term: _____ | My Understanding: | 1 | 2 | 3 | 4

Describe: _____

_____

_____

_____

_____

Draw:

Subject:

Term: _____ | My Understanding: | 1 | 2 | 3 | 4 |

Describe: _____

_____

_____

_____

_____

Draw:

Term: _____ | My Understanding: | 1 | 2 | 3 | 4 |

Describe: _____

_____

_____

_____

_____

Draw:

Term: _____ | My Understanding: | 1 | 2 | 3 | 4

Describe: _____

_____

_____

_____

_____

Draw:

Subject:

Term: _____ | My Understanding: | 1 | 2 | 3 | 4

Describe: _____

_____

_____

_____

_____

Draw:

Subject:

| Term: | My Understanding: | 1 | 2 | 3 | 4 |

Describe:

_____

_____

_____

_____

Draw:

| Term: | My Understanding: | 1 | 2 | 3 | 4 |

Describe:

_____

_____

_____

_____

Draw:

Term: _____ | My Understanding: | 1 | 2 | 3 | 4 |

Describe: _____

_____

_____

_____

_____

Draw:

Subject: _____

Term: _____ | My Understanding: | 1 | 2 | 3 | 4 |

Describe: _____

_____

_____

_____

_____

Draw:

Subject:

Term: _____ | My Understanding: | 1 | 2 | 3 | 4

Describe: _____

_____

_____

_____

Draw:

Term: _____ | My Understanding: | 1 | 2 | 3 | 4

Describe: _____

_____

_____

_____

Draw:

Term: _____ | My Understanding: | 1 | 2 | 3 | 4

Describe: _____

_____

_____

_____

_____

Draw:

Term: _____ | My Understanding: | 1 | 2 | 3 | 4

Describe: _____

_____

_____

_____

_____

Draw:

Subject:

Term: _____ | My Understanding: | 1 | 2 | 3 | 4 |

Describe: _____

_____

_____

_____

Draw:

Subject:

Term: _____ | My Understanding: | 1 | 2 | 3 | 4 |

Describe: _____

_____

_____

_____

Draw:

Term: | My Understanding: | 1 | 2 | 3 | 4

Describe:

_____

_____

_____

_____

Draw:

Subject:

Term: | My Understanding: | 1 | 2 | 3 | 4

Describe:

_____

_____

_____

_____

Draw:

Subject:

Term: _____ | My Understanding: | 1 | 2 | 3 | 4 |

Describe: _____
_____
_____
_____
_____

Draw:

Term: _____ | My Understanding: | 1 | 2 | 3 | 4 |

Describe: _____
_____
_____
_____
_____

Draw:

Subject:

Term: _____ | My Understanding: | 1 | 2 | 3 | 4

Describe: _____

_____

_____

_____

_____

Draw:

Term: _____ | My Understanding: | 1 | 2 | 3 | 4

Describe: _____

_____

_____

_____

_____

Draw:

Term: _____ | My Understanding: | 1 | 2 | 3 | 4 |

Describe: _____

_____

_____

_____

Draw:

Subject:

Term: _____ | My Understanding: | 1 | 2 | 3 | 4 |

Describe: _____

_____

_____

_____

Draw:

Term: _____ | My Understanding: | 1 | 2 | 3 | 4 |

Subject:

Describe: _____

_____

_____

_____

_____

Draw:

Term: _____ | My Understanding: | 1 | 2 | 3 | 4 |

Describe: _____

_____

_____

_____

_____

Draw:

Subject:

Term: _____ | My Understanding: | 1 | 2 | 3 | 4 |

Describe: _____

_____

_____

_____

_____

Draw:

Term: _____ | My Understanding: | 1 | 2 | 3 | 4 |

Describe: _____

_____

_____

_____

_____

Draw:

Term: _____ | My Understanding: | 1 | 2 | 3 | 4

Describe:

_____

_____

_____

_____

Draw:

Subject:

Term: _____ | My Understanding: | 1 | 2 | 3 | 4

Describe:

_____

_____

_____

_____

Draw:

Subject:

Term: _____ | My Understanding: | 1 | 2 | 3 | 4 |

Describe: _____

_____

_____

_____

_____

Draw:

Term: _____ | My Understanding: | 1 | 2 | 3 | 4 |

Describe: _____

_____

_____

_____

_____

Draw:

Term: _____ | My Understanding: | 1 | 2 | 3 | 4 |

Describe: _____

_____

_____

_____

_____

Draw:

Term: _____ | My Understanding: | 1 | 2 | 3 | 4 |

Describe: _____

_____

_____

_____

_____

Draw:

Subject:

Subject:

Term: _____ | My Understanding: | 1 | 2 | 3 | 4 |
Describe: _____
_____
_____
_____
_____

Draw:

Term: _____ | My Understanding: | 1 | 2 | 3 | 4 |
Describe: _____
_____
_____
_____
_____

Draw:

Term: _____ | My Understanding: | 1 | 2 | 3 | 4

Describe:

_____

_____

_____

_____

Draw:

Term: _____ | My Understanding: | 1 | 2 | 3 | 4

Describe:

_____

_____

_____

_____

Draw:

Subject:

Subject:

Term: _____ | My Understanding: | 1 | 2 | 3 | 4 |

Describe: _____

_____

_____

_____

Draw:

Term: _____ | My Understanding: | 1 | 2 | 3 | 4 |

Describe: _____

_____

_____

_____

Draw:

Term: _____ | My Understanding: | 1 | 2 | 3 | 4

Subject:

Describe:

_____

_____

_____

_____

Draw:

Term: _____ | My Understanding: | 1 | 2 | 3 | 4

Describe:

_____

_____

_____

_____

Draw:

Term: _____ | My Understanding: | 1 | 2 | 3 | 4 |

Describe: _____

_____

_____

_____

_____

Draw:

Subject:

Term: _____ | My Understanding: | 1 | 2 | 3 | 4 |

Describe: _____

_____

_____

_____

_____

Draw:

Term: _____ | My Understanding: | 1 | 2 | 3 | 4 |

Describe:

_____

_____

_____

_____

_____

Draw:

Subject:

Term: _____ | My Understanding: | 1 | 2 | 3 | 4 |

Describe:

_____

_____

_____

_____

_____

Draw:

Subject:

Term: _____ | My Understanding: | 1 | 2 | 3 | 4 |
Describe: _____
_____
_____
_____
_____

Draw:

Term: _____ | My Understanding: | 1 | 2 | 3 | 4 |
Describe: _____
_____
_____
_____
_____

Draw:

Term: _____ | My Understanding: | 1 | 2 | 3 | 4 |

Describe: _____

_____

_____

_____

_____

Draw:

Subject:

Term: _____ | My Understanding: | 1 | 2 | 3 | 4 |

Describe: _____

_____

_____

_____

_____

Draw:

Term: _____ | My Understanding: | 1 | 2 | 3 | 4 |

Describe: _____

_____

_____

_____

Draw:

Term: _____ | My Understanding: | 1 | 2 | 3 | 4 |

Describe: _____

_____

_____

_____

Draw:

Subject:

Term: _____ | My Understanding: | 1 | 2 | 3 | 4 |

Describe: _____

_____

_____

_____

Draw:

Subject:

Term: _____ | My Understanding: | 1 | 2 | 3 | 4 |

Describe: _____

_____

_____

_____

Draw:

Term: _____ | My Understanding: | 1 | 2 | 3 | 4 |

Describe: _____

_____

_____

_____

_____

Draw:

Subject:

Term: _____ | My Understanding: | 1 | 2 | 3 | 4 |

Describe: _____

_____

_____

_____

Draw:

Term: _____ | My Understanding: | 1 | 2 | 3 | 4 |

Describe: _____

_____

_____

_____

_____

Draw:

Subject:

Term: _____ | My Understanding: | 1 | 2 | 3 | 4 |

Describe: _____

_____

_____

_____

_____

Draw:

Subject:

Term: _____ | My Understanding: | 1 | 2 | 3 | 4

Describe: _____
_____
_____
_____

Draw:

Term: _____ | My Understanding: | 1 | 2 | 3 | 4

Describe: _____
_____
_____
_____

Draw:

Term: _____ | My Understanding: | 1 | 2 | 3 | 4 |

Describe: _____

_____

_____

_____

_____

Draw:

Subject:

Term: _____ | My Understanding: | 1 | 2 | 3 | 4 |

Describe: _____

_____

_____

_____

_____

Draw:

Subject:

Term: _____ | My Understanding: | 1 | 2 | 3 | 4

Describe: _____
_____
_____
_____
_____

Draw:

Term: _____ | My Understanding: | 1 | 2 | 3 | 4

Describe: _____
_____
_____
_____
_____

Draw:

Term: _____ | My Understanding: | 1 | 2 | 3 | 4 |

Describe: _____

_____

_____

_____

_____

Draw:

Term: _____ | My Understanding: | 1 | 2 | 3 | 4 |

Describe: _____

_____

_____

_____

_____

Draw:

Subject:

Term: _____ | My Understanding: | 1 | 2 | 3 | 4

Describe: _____

_____

_____

_____

_____

Draw:

Term: _____ | My Understanding: | 1 | 2 | 3 | 4

Describe: _____

_____

_____

_____

_____

Draw:

Term: _____ | My Understanding: | 1 | 2 | 3 | 4

Describe: _____

_____

_____

_____

_____

Draw:

Subject:

Term: _____ | My Understanding: | 1 | 2 | 3 | 4

Describe: _____

_____

_____

_____

_____

Draw:

Subject:

Term: _____ | My Understanding: 1 | 2 | 3 | 4

Describe: _____

_____

_____

_____

Draw:

Term: _____ | My Understanding: 1 | 2 | 3 | 4

Describe: _____

_____

_____

_____

Draw:

Term: | My Understanding: | 1 | 2 | 3 | 4

Describe:

_____

_____

_____

_____

Draw:

Subject:

Term: | My Understanding: | 1 | 2 | 3 | 4

Describe:

_____

_____

_____

_____

Draw:

Term: _____ | My Understanding: | 1 | 2 | 3 | 4

Describe: _____

_____

_____

_____

_____

Draw:

Subject:

Term: _____ | My Understanding: | 1 | 2 | 3 | 4

Describe: _____

_____

_____

_____

_____

Draw:

Term: _____ | My Understanding: | 1 | 2 | 3 | 4

Describe:

_____

_____

_____

_____

Draw:

Subject:

Term: _____ | My Understanding: | 1 | 2 | 3 | 4

Describe:

_____

_____

_____

_____

Draw:

Subject:

Term: _____ | My Understanding: | 1 | 2 | 3 | 4

Describe: _____
_____
_____
_____
_____

Draw:

Term: _____ | My Understanding: | 1 | 2 | 3 | 4

Describe: _____
_____
_____
_____
_____

Draw:

Subject: _____

Term: _____ | My Understanding: | 1 | 2 | 3 | 4 |

Describe: _____
_____
_____
_____
_____

Draw:

Term: _____ | My Understanding: | 1 | 2 | 3 | 4 |

Describe: _____
_____
_____
_____
_____

Draw:

Subject:

Term: _____ | My Understanding: | 1 | 2 | 3 | 4

Describe: _____

_____

_____

_____

_____

Draw:

Term: _____ | My Understanding: | 1 | 2 | 3 | 4

Describe: _____

_____

_____

_____

_____

Draw:

Subject: _____

Term: _____ | My Understanding: | 1 | 2 | 3 | 4

Describe: _____

_____

_____

_____

_____

Draw:

Term: _____ | My Understanding: | 1 | 2 | 3 | 4

Describe: _____

_____

_____

_____

_____

Draw:

Subject:

Term: _____ | My Understanding: | 1 | 2 | 3 | 4 |

Describe: _____

_____

_____

_____

_____

Draw:

Term: _____ | My Understanding: | 1 | 2 | 3 | 4 |

Describe: _____

_____

_____

_____

_____

Draw:

Term: _____ | My Understanding: | 1 | 2 | 3 | 4 |

Describe: _____
_____
_____
_____
_____

Draw:

Term: _____ | My Understanding: | 1 | 2 | 3 | 4 |

Describe: _____
_____
_____
_____
_____

Draw:

Subject:

Subject:

Term: _____ | My Understanding: | 1 | 2 | 3 | 4 |

Describe: _____

_____

_____

_____

Draw:

Term: _____ | My Understanding: | 1 | 2 | 3 | 4 |

Describe: _____

_____

_____

_____

Draw:

Term: _____ | My Understanding: | 1 | 2 | 3 | 4 |

Describe: _____

_____

_____

_____

_____

Draw:

Term: _____ | My Understanding: | 1 | 2 | 3 | 4 |

Describe: _____

_____

_____

_____

_____

Draw:

Term: _____ | My Understanding: | 1 | 2 | 3 | 4

Describe: _____

_____

_____

_____

Draw:

Term: _____ | My Understanding: | 1 | 2 | 3 | 4

Describe: _____

_____

_____

_____

Draw:

Subject:

Term: _____ | My Understanding: | 1 | 2 | 3 | 4

Describe: _____

_____

_____

_____

_____

Draw:

Subject:

Term: _____ | My Understanding: | 1 | 2 | 3 | 4

Describe: _____

_____

_____

_____

_____

Draw:

Subject:

Term: _____ | My Understanding: | 1 | 2 | 3 | 4 |

Describe: _____
_____
_____
_____

Draw:

Term: _____ | My Understanding: | 1 | 2 | 3 | 4 |

Describe: _____
_____
_____
_____

Draw:

Term: _____ | My Understanding: | 1 | 2 | 3 | 4

Describe:

_____

_____

_____

_____

Draw:

Subject: _____

Term: _____ | My Understanding: | 1 | 2 | 3 | 4

Describe:

_____

_____

_____

_____

Draw:

Subject:

Term: _____ | My Understanding: | 1 | 2 | 3 | 4

Describe: _____

_____

_____

_____

_____

Draw:

Term: _____ | My Understanding: | 1 | 2 | 3 | 4

Describe: _____

_____

_____

_____

_____

Draw:

Term: _____ | My Understanding: | 1 | 2 | 3 | 4

Subject:

Describe: _____

_____

_____

_____

_____

Draw:

Term: _____ | My Understanding: | 1 | 2 | 3 | 4

Describe: _____

_____

_____

_____

_____

Draw:

Subject:

Term: _____ | My Understanding: | 1 | 2 | 3 | 4 |

Describe: _____
_____
_____
_____

Draw:

Term: _____ | My Understanding: | 1 | 2 | 3 | 4 |

Describe: _____
_____
_____
_____

Draw:

Term: _____ | My Understanding: | 1 | 2 | 3 | 4

Describe:

_____

_____

_____

_____

Draw:

Subject: _____

Term: _____ | My Understanding: | 1 | 2 | 3 | 4

Describe:

_____

_____

_____

_____

Draw:

Subject:

Term: _____ | My Understanding: | 1 | 2 | 3 | 4

Describe: _____

_____

_____

_____

Draw:

Term: _____ | My Understanding: | 1 | 2 | 3 | 4

Describe: _____

_____

_____

_____

Draw:

Term: _____ | My Understanding: | 1 | 2 | 3 | 4

Describe: _____

_____

_____

_____

_____

Draw:

Subject: _____

Term: _____ | My Understanding: | 1 | 2 | 3 | 4

Describe: _____

_____

_____

_____

_____

Draw:

Term: _____ | My Understanding: | 1 | 2 | 3 | 4

Describe: _____
_____
_____
_____
_____

Draw:

Term: _____ | My Understanding: | 1 | 2 | 3 | 4

Describe: _____
_____
_____
_____
_____

Draw:

Subject:

Term: _____ | My Understanding: | 1 | 2 | 3 | 4 |

Describe:

_____

_____

_____

_____

_____

Draw:

Term: _____ | My Understanding: | 1 | 2 | 3 | 4 |

Describe:

_____

_____

_____

_____

_____

Draw:

Subject:

Term: _____ | My Understanding: | 1 | 2 | 3 | 4

Describe: _____

_____

_____

_____

_____

Draw:

Subject:

Term: _____ | My Understanding: | 1 | 2 | 3 | 4

Describe: _____

_____

_____

_____

_____

Draw:

Term: _____ | My Understanding: | 1 | 2 | 3 | 4

Describe: _____

_____

_____

_____

_____

Draw:

Subject:

Term: _____ | My Understanding: | 1 | 2 | 3 | 4

Describe: _____

_____

_____

_____

_____

Draw:

Subject:

Term: _____ | My Understanding: | 1 | 2 | 3 | 4

Describe: _____
_____
_____
_____
_____

Draw:

Term: _____ | My Understanding: | 1 | 2 | 3 | 4

Describe: _____
_____
_____
_____
_____

Draw:

Term: _____ | My Understanding: | 1 | 2 | 3 | 4 |

Describe: _____

_____

_____

_____

_____

Draw:

Subject:

Term: _____ | My Understanding: | 1 | 2 | 3 | 4 |

Describe: _____

_____

_____

_____

_____

Draw:

Subject:

Term: _____ | My Understanding: | 1 | 2 | 3 | 4 |

Describe: _____

_____

_____

_____

_____

Draw:

Term: _____ | My Understanding: | 1 | 2 | 3 | 4 |

Describe: _____

_____

_____

_____

_____

Draw:

Term: _____ | My Understanding: | 1 | 2 | 3 | 4 |

Describe: _____

_____

_____

_____

_____

Draw:

Subject:

Term: _____ | My Understanding: | 1 | 2 | 3 | 4 |

Describe: _____

_____

_____

_____

_____

Draw:

Subject:

Term: _____ | My Understanding: | 1 | 2 | 3 | 4

Describe: _____
_____
_____
_____
_____

Draw:

Term: _____ | My Understanding: | 1 | 2 | 3 | 4

Describe: _____
_____
_____
_____
_____

Draw:

Term: _____ | My Understanding: | 1 | 2 | 3 | 4 |

Describe: _____

_____

_____

_____

_____

Draw:

Subject:

Term: _____ | My Understanding: | 1 | 2 | 3 | 4 |

Describe: _____

_____

_____

_____

_____

Draw:

Subject:

Term: _____ | My Understanding: | 1 | 2 | 3 | 4 |

Describe: _____
_____
_____
_____
_____

Draw:

Term: _____ | My Understanding: | 1 | 2 | 3 | 4 |

Describe: _____
_____
_____
_____
_____

Draw:

Term: _____ | My Understanding: | 1 | 2 | 3 | 4

Describe: _____

_____

_____

_____

_____

Draw:

Term: _____ | My Understanding: | 1 | 2 | 3 | 4

Describe: _____

_____

_____

_____

_____

Draw:

Subject: _____

Subject:

Term: _____ | My Understanding: | 1 | 2 | 3 | 4 |

Describe: _____

_____

_____

_____

_____

Draw:

Term: _____ | My Understanding: | 1 | 2 | 3 | 4 |

Describe: _____

_____

_____

_____

_____

Draw:

Term: _____ | My Understanding: | 1 | 2 | 3 | 4 |

Describe: _____

_____

_____

_____

_____

Draw:

Subject:

Term: _____ | My Understanding: | 1 | 2 | 3 | 4 |

Describe: _____

_____

_____

_____

_____

Draw:

Subject:

Term: _____ | My Understanding: | 1 | 2 | 3 | 4 |

Describe: _____

_____

_____

_____

_____

Draw:

Term: _____ | My Understanding: | 1 | 2 | 3 | 4 |

Describe: _____

_____

_____

_____

_____

Draw:

Term: _____ | My Understanding: | 1 | 2 | 3 | 4 |

Describe: _____

_____

_____

_____

_____

Draw:

Term: _____ | My Understanding: | 1 | 2 | 3 | 4 |

Describe: _____

_____

_____

_____

_____

Draw:

Subject:

Subject:

Term: _____ | My Understanding: | 1 | 2 | 3 | 4 |

Describe: _____

_____

_____

_____

_____

Draw:

Term: _____ | My Understanding: | 1 | 2 | 3 | 4 |

Describe: _____

_____

_____

_____

_____

Draw:

Subject:

Term: _____ | My Understanding: | 1 | 2 | 3 | 4 |

Describe: _____
_____
_____
_____
_____

Draw:

Term: _____ | My Understanding: | 1 | 2 | 3 | 4 |

Describe: _____
_____
_____
_____
_____

Draw:

Subject:

Term: _____ | My Understanding: | 1 | 2 | 3 | 4 |

Describe: _____

_____

_____

_____

Draw:

Term: _____ | My Understanding: | 1 | 2 | 3 | 4 |

Describe: _____

_____

_____

_____

Draw:

Term: _____ | My Understanding: | 1 | 2 | 3 | 4 |

Describe:

_____

_____

_____

_____

Draw:

Subject:

Term: _____ | My Understanding: | 1 | 2 | 3 | 4 |

Describe:

_____

_____

_____

_____

Draw:

Subject:

Term: _____ | My Understanding: 1 | 2 | 3 | 4

Describe: _____
_____
_____
_____
_____

Draw:

Term: _____ | My Understanding: 1 | 2 | 3 | 4

Describe: _____
_____
_____
_____

Draw:

Term: _____ | My Understanding: | 1 | 2 | 3 | 4 |

Subject: _____

Describe: _____
_____
_____
_____
_____

Draw:

Term: _____ | My Understanding: | 1 | 2 | 3 | 4 |

Describe: _____
_____
_____
_____
_____

Draw:

Subject:

Term: _____ | My Understanding: | 1 | 2 | 3 | 4

Describe: _____
_____
_____
_____

Draw:

Term: _____ | My Understanding: | 1 | 2 | 3 | 4

Describe: _____
_____
_____
_____

Draw:

Term: _____ | My Understanding: | 1 | 2 | 3 | 4

Subject:

Describe:

_____

_____

_____

_____

Draw:

Term: _____ | My Understanding: | 1 | 2 | 3 | 4

Describe:

_____

_____

_____

_____

Draw:

Subject:

Term: _____ | My Understanding: 1 | 2 | 3 | 4

Describe: _____

_____

_____

_____

_____

Draw:

Term: _____ | My Understanding: 1 | 2 | 3 | 4

Describe: _____

_____

_____

_____

_____

Draw:

Term: _____ | My Understanding: | 1 | 2 | 3 | 4 | Subject:

Describe:

_____

_____

_____

_____

Draw:

Term: _____ | My Understanding: | 1 | 2 | 3 | 4 |

Describe:

_____

_____

_____

_____

Draw:

Subject:

Term: _____ | My Understanding: | 1 | 2 | 3 | 4 |

Describe: _____

_____

_____

_____

_____

Draw:

Term: _____ | My Understanding: | 1 | 2 | 3 | 4 |

Describe: _____

_____

_____

_____

_____

Draw:

Term: _____ | My Understanding: | 1 | 2 | 3 | 4 | **Subject:**

Describe:

_____

_____

_____

_____

Draw:

Term: _____ | My Understanding: | 1 | 2 | 3 | 4 |

Describe:

_____

_____

_____

_____

Draw:

Subject:

Term: _____ | My Understanding: | 1 | 2 | 3 | 4

Describe:
_____
_____
_____
_____

Draw:

Term: _____ | My Understanding: | 1 | 2 | 3 | 4

Describe:
_____
_____
_____
_____

Draw:

Term: _____ | My Understanding: | 1 | 2 | 3 | 4

Describe: _____

_____

_____

_____

_____

Draw:

Subject: _____

Term: _____ | My Understanding: | 1 | 2 | 3 | 4

Describe: _____

_____

_____

_____

_____

Draw:

Subject:

Term: _____ | My Understanding: | 1 | 2 | 3 | 4

Describe: _____

_____

_____

_____

_____

Draw:

Term: _____ | My Understanding: | 1 | 2 | 3 | 4

Describe: _____

_____

_____

_____

_____

Draw:

Term: _____ | My Understanding: | 1 | 2 | 3 | 4

Describe:

_____

_____

_____

_____

Draw:

Subject:

Term: _____ | My Understanding: | 1 | 2 | 3 | 4

Describe:

_____

_____

_____

_____

Draw:

Subject:

Term: _____ | My Understanding: | 1 | 2 | 3 | 4 |

Describe: _____
_____
_____
_____
_____

Draw:

Term: _____ | My Understanding: | 1 | 2 | 3 | 4 |

Describe: _____
_____
_____
_____
_____

Draw:

Term: _____ | My Understanding: | 1 | 2 | 3 | 4 |

Describe:

_____

_____

_____

_____

Draw:

Subject:

Term: _____ | My Understanding: | 1 | 2 | 3 | 4 |

Describe:

_____

_____

_____

_____

Draw:

Subject:

Term: _____ | My Understanding: | 1 | 2 | 3 | 4

Describe:
_____
_____
_____
_____

Draw:

Term: _____ | My Understanding: | 1 | 2 | 3 | 4

Describe:
_____
_____
_____
_____

Draw:

Term: _____ | My Understanding: | 1 | 2 | 3 | 4 |

Describe: _____

_____

_____

_____

Draw:

Term: _____ | My Understanding: | 1 | 2 | 3 | 4 |

Describe: _____

_____

_____

_____

Draw:

Subject:

Subject:

Term: _____ | My Understanding: | 1 | 2 | 3 | 4

Describe: _____
_____
_____
_____
_____

Draw:

Term: _____ | My Understanding: | 1 | 2 | 3 | 4

Describe: _____
_____
_____
_____
_____

Draw:

Term: _____ | My Understanding: | 1 | 2 | 3 | 4 |

Describe:

_____

_____

_____

_____

Draw:

Term: _____ | My Understanding: | 1 | 2 | 3 | 4 |

Describe:

_____

_____

_____

_____

Draw:

Subject:

Subject:

Term: _____ | My Understanding: | 1 | 2 | 3 | 4

Describe: _____

_____

_____

_____

Draw:

Term: _____ | My Understanding: | 1 | 2 | 3 | 4

Describe: _____

_____

_____

_____

Draw:

Term: _____ | My Understanding: | 1 | 2 | 3 | 4

Describe:

_____

_____

_____

_____

Draw:

Subject:

Term: _____ | My Understanding: | 1 | 2 | 3 | 4

Describe:

_____

_____

_____

_____

Draw:

Subject:

Term: _____ | My Understanding: | 1 | 2 | 3 | 4

Describe: _____

_____

_____

_____

_____

Draw:

Term: _____ | My Understanding: | 1 | 2 | 3 | 4

Describe: _____

_____

_____

_____

_____

Draw:

Term: _____ | My Understanding: | 1 | 2 | 3 | 4

Describe: _____

_____

_____

_____

_____

Draw:

Subject:

Term: _____ | My Understanding: | 1 | 2 | 3 | 4

Describe: _____

_____

_____

_____

_____

Draw:

Subject:

Term: _____ | My Understanding: | 1 | 2 | 3 | 4 |

Describe: _____

_____

_____

_____

_____

Draw:

Term: _____ | My Understanding: | 1 | 2 | 3 | 4 |

Describe: _____

_____

_____

_____

_____

Draw:

Term: _____ | My Understanding: | 1 | 2 | 3 | 4 |

Describe: _____

_____

_____

_____

_____

Draw:

Subject: _____

Term: _____ | My Understanding: | 1 | 2 | 3 | 4 |

Describe: _____

_____

_____

_____

_____

Draw:

Subject:

Term: _____ | My Understanding: | 1 | 2 | 3 | 4

Describe: _____

_____

_____

_____

_____

Draw:

Term: _____ | My Understanding: | 1 | 2 | 3 | 4

Describe: _____

_____

_____

_____

_____

Draw:

Term: _____ | My Understanding: | 1 | 2 | 3 | 4 |

Subject:

Describe: _____
_____
_____
_____
_____

Draw:

Term: _____ | My Understanding: | 1 | 2 | 3 | 4 |

Describe: _____
_____
_____
_____
_____

Draw:

Subject:

Term: _____ | My Understanding: | 1 | 2 | 3 | 4

Describe: _____

_____

_____

_____

_____

Draw:

Term: _____ | My Understanding: | 1 | 2 | 3 | 4

Describe: _____

_____

_____

_____

_____

Draw:

Term: _____ | My Understanding: | 1 | 2 | 3 | 4

Describe: _____

_____

_____

_____

_____

Draw:

Term: _____ | My Understanding: | 1 | 2 | 3 | 4

Describe: _____

_____

_____

_____

_____

Draw:

Term: _____ | My Understanding: | 1 | 2 | 3 | 4

Describe: _____

_____

_____

_____

_____

Draw:

Term: _____ | My Understanding: | 1 | 2 | 3 | 4

Describe: _____

_____

_____

_____

Draw:

Subject:

Term: _____ | My Understanding: | 1 | 2 | 3 | 4 |

Describe: _____

_____

_____

_____

_____

Draw:

Subject:

Term: _____ | My Understanding: | 1 | 2 | 3 | 4 |

Describe: _____

_____

_____

_____

Draw:

Term: | My Understanding: 1 | 2 | 3 | 4

Describe:

_____

_____

_____

_____

Draw:

Subject:

Term: | My Understanding: 1 | 2 | 3 | 4

Describe:

_____

_____

_____

_____

Draw:

Term: _____ | My Understanding: | 1 | 2 | 3 | 4 |

Describe: _____

_____

_____

_____

Draw:

Subject:

Term: _____ | My Understanding: | 1 | 2 | 3 | 4 |

Describe: _____

_____

_____

_____

Draw:

Term: _____ | My Understanding: | 1 | 2 | 3 | 4

Describe: _____

_____

_____

_____

_____

Draw:

Subject:

Term: _____ | My Understanding: | 1 | 2 | 3 | 4

Describe: _____

_____

_____

_____

_____

Draw:

Term: _____ | My Understanding: | 1 | 2 | 3 | 4 |

Describe: _____

_____

_____

_____

_____

Draw:

Term: _____ | My Understanding: | 1 | 2 | 3 | 4 |

Describe: _____

_____

_____

_____

_____

Draw:

Subject:

Term: _____ | My Understanding: | 1 | 2 | 3 | 4 |

Describe: _____

_____

_____

_____

Draw:

Term: _____ | My Understanding: | 1 | 2 | 3 | 4 |

Describe: _____

_____

_____

_____

Draw:

Term: _____ | My Understanding: | 1 | 2 | 3 | 4 |

Describe: _____

_____

_____

_____

_____

Draw:

Term: _____ | My Understanding: | 1 | 2 | 3 | 4 |

Describe: _____

_____

_____

_____

_____

Draw:

Subject: _____

Subject:

Term: _____ | My Understanding: | 1 | 2 | 3 | 4 |

Describe: _____

_____

_____

_____

_____

Draw:

Term: _____ | My Understanding: | 1 | 2 | 3 | 4 |

Describe: _____

_____

_____

_____

Draw:

Term: _____ | My Understanding: | 1 | 2 | 3 | 4

Describe:

_____

_____

_____

_____

Draw:

Term: _____ | My Understanding: | 1 | 2 | 3 | 4

Describe:

_____

_____

_____

_____

Draw:

Subject:

Subject:

Term: _____ | My Understanding: | 1 | 2 | 3 | 4 |

Describe: _____

_____

_____

_____

_____

Draw:

Term: _____ | My Understanding: | 1 | 2 | 3 | 4 |

Describe: _____

_____

_____

_____

_____

Draw:

Term: _____ | My Understanding: | 1 | 2 | 3 | 4

Describe:
_____
_____
_____
_____
_____

Draw:

Subject:

Term: _____ | My Understanding: | 1 | 2 | 3 | 4

Describe:
_____
_____
_____
_____
_____

Draw:

Term: _____ | My Understanding: | 1 | 2 | 3 | 4 |

Describe: _____

_____

_____

_____

Draw:

Term: _____ | My Understanding: | 1 | 2 | 3 | 4 |

Describe: _____

_____

_____

_____

Draw:

Subject:

Term: _____ | My Understanding: | 1 | 2 | 3 | 4

Describe: _____

_____

_____

_____

_____

Draw:

Subject: _____

Term: _____ | My Understanding: | 1 | 2 | 3 | 4

Describe: _____

_____

_____

_____

_____

Draw:

Subject:

Term: _____ | My Understanding: | 1 | 2 | 3 | 4 |

Describe:
_____
_____
_____
_____
_____

Draw:

Term: _____ | My Understanding: | 1 | 2 | 3 | 4 |

Describe:
_____
_____
_____
_____
_____

Draw:

Term: _____ | My Understanding: | 1 | 2 | 3 | 4 | Subject:

Describe: _____

_____

_____

_____

_____

Draw:

Term: _____ | My Understanding: | 1 | 2 | 3 | 4 |

Describe: _____

_____

_____

_____

_____

Draw:

Subject:

Term: _____ | My Understanding: | 1 | 2 | 3 | 4

Describe: _____
_____
_____
_____

Draw:

Term: _____ | My Understanding: | 1 | 2 | 3 | 4

Describe: _____
_____
_____
_____

Draw:

Term: _____ | My Understanding: | 1 | 2 | 3 | 4 |

Describe: _____

_____

_____

_____

_____

Draw:

Term: _____ | My Understanding: | 1 | 2 | 3 | 4 |

Describe: _____

_____

_____

_____

_____

Draw:

Subject: _____

Subject:

Term: _____ | My Understanding: | 1 | 2 | 3 | 4

Describe: _____

Draw:

Term: _____ | My Understanding: | 1 | 2 | 3 | 4

Describe: _____

Draw:

Term: _____ | My Understanding: | 1 | 2 | 3 | 4 |

Describe: _____

_____

_____

_____

_____

Draw:

Subject:

Term: _____ | My Understanding: | 1 | 2 | 3 | 4 |

Describe: _____

_____

_____

_____

_____

Draw:

Subject:

Term: _____ | My Understanding: | 1 | 2 | 3 | 4

Describe: _____

_____

_____

_____

Draw:

Term: _____ | My Understanding: | 1 | 2 | 3 | 4

Describe: _____

_____

_____

_____

Draw:

Term: | My Understanding: | 1 | 2 | 3 | 4

Describe: _____

_____

_____

_____

_____

Draw:

Term: | My Understanding: | 1 | 2 | 3 | 4

Describe: _____

_____

_____

_____

_____

Draw:

Subject:

Term: _____ | My Understanding: | 1 | 2 | 3 | 4

Describe: _____
_____
_____
_____
_____

Draw:

Term: _____ | My Understanding: | 1 | 2 | 3 | 4

Describe: _____
_____
_____
_____
_____

Draw:

Term: _____ | My Understanding: | 1 | 2 | 3 | 4

Describe: _____

_____

_____

_____

_____

Draw:

Term: _____ | My Understanding: | 1 | 2 | 3 | 4

Describe: _____

_____

_____

_____

_____

Draw:

Subject:

Subject:

| Term: | My Understanding: | 1 | 2 | 3 | 4 |

Describe: _____

_____

_____

_____

Draw:

| Term: | My Understanding: | 1 | 2 | 3 | 4 |

Describe: _____

_____

_____

_____

Draw:

Term: _____ | My Understanding: | 1 | 2 | 3 | 4 |

Subject: _____

Describe: _____

_____

_____

_____

_____

Draw:

Term: _____ | My Understanding: | 1 | 2 | 3 | 4 |

Describe: _____

_____

_____

_____

_____

Draw:

Subject:

Term: _____ | My Understanding: | 1 | 2 | 3 | 4

Describe: _____

_____

_____

_____

Draw:

Term: _____ | My Understanding: | 1 | 2 | 3 | 4

Describe: _____

_____

_____

_____

Draw:

Subject:

Term: _____ | My Understanding: | 1 | 2 | 3 | 4

Describe: _____
_____
_____
_____

Draw:

Term: _____ | My Understanding: | 1 | 2 | 3 | 4

Describe: _____
_____
_____
_____

Draw:

Subject:

Term: _____ | My Understanding: | 1 | 2 | 3 | 4

Describe: _____

_____

_____

_____

_____

Draw:

Term: _____ | My Understanding: | 1 | 2 | 3 | 4

Describe: _____

_____

_____

_____

_____

Draw:

Term: _____ | My Understanding: | 1 | 2 | 3 | 4 |

Describe: _____

_____

_____

_____

_____

Draw:

Subject: _____

Term: _____ | My Understanding: | 1 | 2 | 3 | 4 |

Describe: _____

_____

_____

_____

_____

Draw:

Subject:

Term: _____ | My Understanding: | 1 | 2 | 3 | 4

Describe: _____

_____

_____

_____

_____

Draw:

Term: _____ | My Understanding: | 1 | 2 | 3 | 4

Describe: _____

_____

_____

_____

_____

Draw:

Term: _____ | My Understanding: | 1 | 2 | 3 | 4

Describe:

_____

_____

_____

_____

Draw:

Term: _____ | My Understanding: | 1 | 2 | 3 | 4

Describe:

_____

_____

_____

_____

Draw:

Subject:

Term: _____ | My Understanding: | 1 | 2 | 3 | 4

Describe: _____
_____
_____
_____

Draw:

Term: _____ | My Understanding: | 1 | 2 | 3 | 4

Describe: _____
_____
_____
_____

Draw:

Term: _____ | My Understanding: | 1 | 2 | 3 | 4 |

Describe: _____

_____

_____

_____

_____

Draw:

Subject:

Term: _____ | My Understanding: | 1 | 2 | 3 | 4 |

Describe: _____

_____

_____

_____

_____

Draw:

Subject:

Term: _____ | My Understanding: | 1 | 2 | 3 | 4 |

Describe: _____
_____
_____
_____
_____

Draw:

Term: _____ | My Understanding: | 1 | 2 | 3 | 4 |

Describe: _____
_____
_____
_____
_____

Draw:

Term: _____ | My Understanding: | 1 | 2 | 3 | 4 |

Describe: _____

_____

_____

_____

_____

Draw:

Subject:

Term: _____ | My Understanding: | 1 | 2 | 3 | 4 |

Describe: _____

_____

_____

_____

_____

Draw:

Subject:

Term: _____ | My Understanding: | 1 | 2 | 3 | 4

Describe: _____
_____
_____
_____
_____

Draw:

Term: _____ | My Understanding: | 1 | 2 | 3 | 4

Describe: _____
_____
_____
_____
_____

Draw:

Term: _____ | My Understanding: | 1 | 2 | 3 | 4 |

Describe: _____

_____

_____

_____

Draw:

Subject:

Term: _____ | My Understanding: | 1 | 2 | 3 | 4 |

Describe: _____

_____

_____

_____

Draw:

Subject:

Term: _____ | My Understanding: | 1 | 2 | 3 | 4 |

Describe: _____
_____
_____
_____
_____

Draw:

Term: _____ | My Understanding: | 1 | 2 | 3 | 4 |

Describe: _____
_____
_____
_____
_____

Draw:

Subject:

Term: _____ | My Understanding: | 1 | 2 | 3 | 4 |

Describe: _____

_____

_____

_____

Draw:

Term: _____ | My Understanding: | 1 | 2 | 3 | 4 |

Describe: _____

_____

_____

_____

Draw:

Subject:

Term: _____ | My Understanding: | 1 | 2 | 3 | 4

Describe: _____
_____
_____
_____

Draw:

Term: _____ | My Understanding: | 1 | 2 | 3 | 4

Describe: _____
_____
_____
_____

Draw:

Subject:

Term: _____ | My Understanding: | 1 | 2 | 3 | 4 |

Describe:
_____
_____
_____
_____
_____

Draw:

Term: _____ | My Understanding: | 1 | 2 | 3 | 4 |

Describe:
_____
_____
_____
_____
_____

Draw:

Subject:

Term: _____ | My Understanding: | 1 | 2 | 3 | 4 |

Describe: _____

_____

_____

_____

_____

Draw:

Term: _____ | My Understanding: | 1 | 2 | 3 | 4 |

Describe: _____

_____

_____

_____

_____

Draw:

Term: _____ | My Understanding: | 1 | 2 | 3 | 4 |

Describe: _____

_____

_____

_____

Draw:

Subject:

Term: _____ | My Understanding: | 1 | 2 | 3 | 4 |

Describe: _____

_____

_____

_____

Draw:

Subject:

Term: _____ | My Understanding: | 1 | 2 | 3 | 4

Describe: _____
_____
_____
_____
_____

Draw:

Term: _____ | My Understanding: | 1 | 2 | 3 | 4

Describe: _____
_____
_____
_____
_____

Draw: